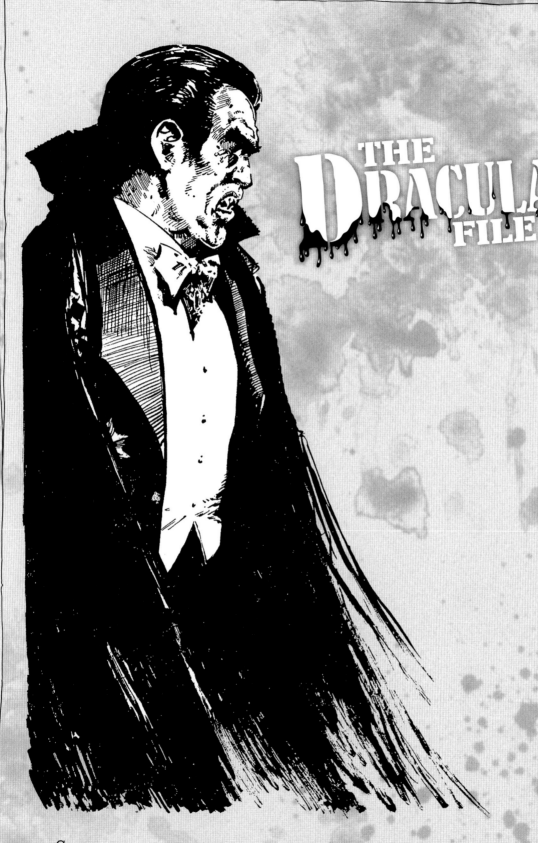

THE DRACULA FILE

Created by **Gerry Finley-Day** & **Eric Bradbury**

"Greetings once again, mortals..."

That would be the unearthly voice of Ghastly McNasty, SCREAM!'s inhuman editor, uttering his familiar reader welcome from The Depths where he put together each chilling issue of the short-lived though well-regarded comic.

SCREAM! was a 32-page weekly title from 1984 featuring horror stories. It was laid to rest in the cemetery of cancelled comics after an industrial dispute at publishers IPC Magazines. Yet suitably, given SCREAM!'s subject matter, several of its most revered stories have risen from the grave to reappear in special collections, such as the one you are holding now.

The Dracula File is a vampire tale given a pleasing, 1980s twist by primary writer and renowned comics creator Gerry Finley-Day. With tensions high between NATO forces and the Warsaw Pact, Gerry adds some extra chills to the Cold War with his Nosferatu emerging from behind the Iron Curtain to spread terror to the west. The result is an appealing mix of clever updates to Bram Stoker's creation interwoven with some classic conventions of vampire mythology.

In terms of artwork for the story, SCREAM! simply could not have found a more fitting contributor than Eric Bradbury. The grimly atmospheric and eerie renderings of the master comic-strip draughtsman shift this already intriguing storyline to another dimension.

When SCREAM! was being put together, it was felt **The Dracula File**, featuring such a legendary villain of the genre, would be an important serial for the title. The opening episode was given primary position on page 3, and had the unusual distinction of being 5 pages long. Reader feedback at the time revealed the story to be hugely popular, while it appears to be one of those comic-strips which lived long in the memory of those who read it first time around.

So then, let's re-open **The Dracula File** again...but remember, like all SCREAM! stories, it's Not For The Nervous!

Ian Rimmer,
Editor (when Ghastly wasn't looking), SCREAM!

Script: Gerry Finley-Day

Simon Furman

Art:
Eric Bradbury

Letters:
John Aldrich
P. Knight

THESE CELLARS CONTAIN PACKING-CASES THAT HAVE LAIN HERE FOR DECADES...

...SENT HERE FOR JUST SUCH A DAY AS THIS!

YES! HERE IT IS... THE EARTH OF MY NATIVE LAND... THE KEY TO MY SURVIVAL! HURRY, WOMAN— IT IS ALMOST DAWN!

LESS THAN AN HOUR LATER...

MORNING ROUNDS—BETTER CHECK OUR NEW GUEST.

NO!

HE MUST REMAIN UNDISTURBED ALL DAY! I SEDATED HIM— HE WAS SUFFERING FROM SHOCK AFTER HIS ORDEAL!

A WHOLE DAY? THE INTELLIGENCE BODS WON'T LIKE THAT, NURSE!

SHE'S IN A FUNNY MOOD THIS MORNING...

AND DID YOU SEE THAT DIRT ON HER DRESS? SHE'S USUALLY NEAT AND TIDY!

IN WHITEHALL...

IT'S UNFORTUNATE OUR NEW DEFECTOR IS NOT AVAILABLE FOR QUESTIONING UNTIL TONIGHT. BUT JUST MAKE SURE YOU KEEP HIM SAFE – THE KGB WILL KNOW WE HAVE HIM!

...URE ENOUGH, IN A SIMILAR BUILDING IN EASTERN EUROPE...

THE, ER – OLD BOOKS YOU WANTED, COMRADE-COLONEL.

A WARSAW-PACT INTELLIGENCE OFFICER KNEW THE TRUTH ABOUT THE DEFECTOR...

I AM SURE HE IS A VAMPIRE... BUT I AM ORDERED NOT TO WARN THE WEST – TO LET THEM PAY THE PRICE FOR WELCOMING DEFECTORS. YET THIS IS BEYOND POLITICS!

I WAS RIGHT! EVEN THE NOSFERATU MUST OBEY CERTAIN LAWS... THE KEY IS SOIL!

THE VAMPIRE NEEDS HIS OWN HOMELAND'S SOIL TO SURVIVE — LIKE A POISONOUS PLANT!

AND WITHOUT THAT SOIL HE CANNOT LAST ONE DAY! I CAN RELAX... NO REIGN OF TERROR WILL START IN BRITAIN!

BUT THAT NIGHT, HUNDREDS OF MILES TO THE WEST...

HE HAS GONE. MY LORD HAS RESTED AND EXPLORES HIS NEW HUNTING-GROUND!

AND...

FOX BARKING FROM THAT COPSE. I'LL MAKE SURE HE DOESN'T GET INTO ANY MORE CHICKEN-COOPS!

GOT YOU, YER BRUTE! GET THE CARCASS, CAESAR!

WH—WHO ARE YOU?

I AM YOUR DEATH!

Next Week: Into the Master's Lair!

T MOXON HALL...

VERY GOOD, SIR. WE'LL EXPECT YOU THIS EVENING. WE'LL HAVE HIM READY FOR INTERVIEWING.

MEN COMING TO SEE THE MASTER. IT HAD TO HAPPEN! HOW DO I PREVENT THEM GETTING SUSPICIOUS?

ONITORING SERVICES LISTENED TO ALL ESTERN NEWS BROADCASTS...

YOU WISH FOR REPORTS OF ANY MYSTERIOUS KILLINGS IN BRITAIN, COMRADE COLONEL?

YES!

MEANWHILE, BEHIND THE IRON CURTAIN, A KGB OFFICER WAS MORE THAN SUSPICIOUS...

THE NOSFERATU'S SECOND DAY IN BRITAIN — BUT HE MUST NO LONGER EXIST, FOR EVEN HE MUST OBEY THE RULES...

NOSFERATU:— RUMANIAN FOR 'UNDEAD'.

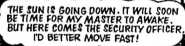

LATER THAT SAME DAY, AT MOXON HALL...

THE SUN IS GOING DOWN. IT WILL SOON BE TIME FOR MY MASTER TO AWAKE. BUT HERE COMES THE SECURITY OFFICER. I'D BETTER MOVE FAST!

...AND THOSE RULES STATE THAT HE NEEDS HIS NATIVE SOIL TO REMAIN ALIVE. NO SUCH SOIL EXISTS IN BRITAIN SO HE MUST HAVE PERISHED! YET I HAVE TO BE SURE.

MONITORING SECTION HERE, COMRADE.

NURSE, LET'S GET HIM DRESSED AND — WHAT THE-? THE ROOM'S EMPTY!

YES, HE IS ELSEWHERE IN THE HOUSE. FOLLOW ME...

WHAT ARE YOU PLAYING AT? THESE ARE THE CELLARS! HAVE YOU GONE DAFT, NURSE? HE CAN'T BE DOWN HERE!

JUST THROUGH THIS DOOR!

WHAT'S THAT OVER THERE?

TAKE A CLOSER LOOK!

LATER, IN A NEARBY ALLEY, THE BAT CHANGED ITS FORM, INTO DRACULA!

THE LEGENDARY VAMPIRE OF EASTERN EUROPE HAD ARRIVED IN BRITAIN A FEW NIGHTS BEFORE...

THE NIGHT IS YOUNG. THERE ARE VICTIMS TO BE CLAIMED ON EVERY STREET!

NEARBY...

COME ON! THE PARTY'S JUST STARTED!

I LOVE FANCY DRESS PARTIES!

LIGHTS - I MUST TURN AWAY!

PULL OVER - WE'RE HERE!

THIS WAY, MATE — HURRY, OR YOU'LL MISS THE FUN!

COME ON IN!

SO YOU INVITE ME ACROSS YOUR THRESHOLD? VERY WELL...

THIS WAY!

A MASKED BALL— LIKE THOSE HELD IN THE CASTLES OF MY HOMELAND...

THE VAMPIRE TORE OFF THE COSTUME HEAD...

INFANTILE FOOL— NOW YOU SHALL KNOW THE REAL MEANING OF FEAR!

AIEEEEE!

LONG MOMENTS LATER...

DRAC'S BACK, BUT WHERE'S HARRY? HE'S NORMALLY THE LIFE AND SOUL OF THE PARTY!

NOW HE IS THIS PARTY'S FIRST DEATH!

HEY, DUKE— WANNA DANCE?

MY CORRECT TITLE IS 'COUNT', MY PRETTY YOUNG FRIEND!

LATER...

THIS WILL HAVE TO BE THE LAST DANCE, I'VE GOT TO GET HOME!

IT CERTAINLY WILL BE YOUR LAST DANCE!

YOU GOING MY WAY? WE CAN SHARE A TAXI!

CARRIAGE, YOU MEAN...

A "CARRIAGE"? SAY, YOU'RE REALLY INTO THE PART, AREN'T YOU?

IN YOU GET, MATE!

SLOANE STREET, PLEASE, DRIVER...

AGAIN I AM INVITED INSIDE... SUCH HOSPITALITY CAN HAVE ONLY ONE REWARD... DEATH!

Next Instalment: Discovery!

IT'S...A HOUND FROM HELL!

THE VAN WENT OUT OF CONTROL AND THERE WAS A FEARFUL COLLISION...

A DAZED GUARD STAGGERED TO THE REAR OF THE SECOND VAN...

B-BETTER CHECK THE PRISONERS ARE OKAY...

BUT CAPTAIN BLACK AND NURSE NIGHTINGALE WERE WAITING...

WE HAVE HIM NURSE! I KNEW THE MASTER WOULD MAKE SHORT WORK OF THEM! WE ARE FREE!

THE ONLY UNTOUCHED POLICEMAN WAS A MOTORCYCLE-OUTRIDER, AT THE REAR OF THE CONVOY...

CAN'T BE AN ACCIDENT, IT MUST BE AN AMBUSH! GOT TO GET HELP— FAST!

I'LL OPEN THE BIKE UP SO NOTHING CAN CATCH ME!

A QUICK GLANCE IN HIS REAR VIEW MIRROR ASSURED THE DRIVER THERE WAS NOTHING BEHIND HIM...

BUT VAMPIRES CAST NO REFLECTION!

UUUAAARGH!

THE OTHERS FLED FROM THE HORRIFIC SCENE...

RUN — LIKE THE SCARED RABBITS YOU REALLY ARE!

TH-THANKS FOR SAVING ME, MISTER.

SAVING YOU? OH, NO...YOU DON'T UNDERSTAND...

...I WAS ONLY SAVING YOU FOR MYSELF!

AFTER THE VAMPIRE HAD DRUNK HIS FILL, HE TURNED TO RAY LOGAN, THE YOUTH HE HAD HURLED AWAY FROM HIM DURING THE FIGHT...

UNNGH!

AH, YOU ARE STILL ALIVE! YOU MUST BE A MORE STURDY SPECIMEN THAN MOST...

AFTER THE INCOMPETENCE DEMONSTRATED BY MY OTHER SLAVES, I HAVE NEED OF A NEW HUMAN SERVANT!

MY MARK IS NOW UPON YOU. YOU WILL SERVE ME FROM THIS DAY ON!

THE VAMPIRE HAD THE POWER TO CREATE STILL-HUMAN SLAVES BY DRAWING ONLY A LITTLE BLOOD.

LATER THAT NIGHT, IN THE FUNERAL PARLOUR RUN BY RONALD STUART...

HUH? SOMEONE'S STOLEN ONE OF MY COFFINS. WHO WOULD WANT TO STEAL ONE OF THOSE?

CAPTAIN BLACK AND NURSE NIGHTINGALE HAD ENSURED THAT THEIR MASTER WOULD REST WELL WHEN SUNRISE CAME!

FOR OTHERS, REST WAS NOT THE ORDER OF THE NEXT DAY...

ALL IS READY!

STAKIS HAD BOOKED INTO A SMALL HOTEL. THERE HE WENT ABOUT HIS PREPARATIONS...

A WOODEN STAKE THROUGH THE HEART... JUST ONE OF THE WAYS TO KILL A VAMPIRE!

I HAVE ALL I NEED...STAKES, GARLIC, HOLY WATER, A CROSS... NOW THE HUNT CAN BEGIN!

Next instalment: Trail of the vampire!

THE DRACULA FILE

DRACULA, THE VAMPIRE OF LEGEND, HAD COME TO BRITAIN AS A DEFECTOR FROM THE EAST. NOW HE WAS IN LONDON, AND ALREADY LEAVING A GRISLY TRAIL...

DAILY POST

BIKE BOYS BUTCHERED

The Bugle

GANG KILLED IN MYSTERY ATTACK

DAILY CLARION

POLICE DEATHS — COULD THEY HAVE BEEN DELIBERATE

The News

SCREAM

SCRIPT: KEN NOBLE
ART: E. BRADBURY
LETTERING: J. ALDRICH

THESE BRITISH PEOPLE WOULD NEVER BELIEVE THIS WAS ALL THE WORK OF A VAMPIRE! HE IS HERE, IN THE CITY... AND I MUST SEEK HIM OUT!

A FEW MILES AWAY...

HE SLEEPS WELL IN THE COFFIN WE STOLE FOR HIM!

AND HE HAD A GOOD NIGHT'S HUNTING — OUR LORD IS SATISFIED!

WE MUST KEEP WATCH WHILE HIS POWERS ARE WEAK IN THE DAYLIGHT HOURS. NO-ONE MUST COME NEAR...

COLONEL STAKIS, EX-KGB OFFICER, HAD PURSUED DRACULA FROM EASTERN EUROPE, ARMING HIMSELF WITH THE TRADITIONAL WEAPONS OF THE VAMPIRE-HUNTER...

CAPTAIN BLACK AND NURSE NIGHTINGALE, TWO BRITISH INTELLIGENCE PEOPLE WHO HAD RECEIVED DRACULA ON HIS ENTRY TO BRITAIN, HAD BEEN HIS FIRST VICTIMS AND WERE NOW HIS SLAVES...

DEED, A FEW MILES AWAY...

THE—THE BEST I COULD FIND FOR YOU, MASTER...

OLD RUINS...

THIS PROPERTY IS CONDEMNED

DRACULA HAD TWO OTHER SLAVES...

THE PLACE IS DERELICT, MASTER. NOBODY AROUND...

WRONG— I HEAR SOUNDS BELOW!

THERE ARE PEOPLE HERE. HOW CLEVER OF YOU TO FIND A LAIR WITH ITS OWN FOOD SUPPLY!

GIZ A SWIG, SCOTTIE!

THAT'S MA BOTTLE!

GIZ IT HERE, I SAID!

NEXT SECOND—

PAAHH! THEIR BLOOD IS TAINTED BY FOUL ALCOHOL!

YE GODS! WHAT IS IT?

I'M NOT STAYIN' TO FIND OUT!

ARRGH! ME NECK! SOMETHING'S BITIN' ME!

IT'S A BIRD!

NAH— IT'S A BAT!

'TAIN'T NATURAL! RUN FOR IT!

MASTER— LEAVE THEM BE! THEY'RE NO USE TO YOU!

INSIDE THE BUS, THE MIRROR BY THE STAIRS JUST SHOWED ROWS OF EMPTY SEATS...

I CAN SIT DOWN AND—HUH? WHAT'S THAT SOUND UPSTAIRS? WE'VE **NO** PASSENGERS!

THE CONDUCTOR CLIMBED THE STAIRS AND...

WHAT'S YOUR GAME? HIDIN' BEHIND THE SEATS SO YOU DON'T SHOW UP IN THE MIRROR..?

YOU HEAR ME, MATE. I WANT YOU OFF! IT'S THE END OF THE LINE!

FOR **YOU** IT MOST CERTAINLY IS, PEASANT!

AAAAARGH!

MOMENTS LATER...

NOW I LEAVE IN SECRET—MY PRESENCE UNWITNESSED

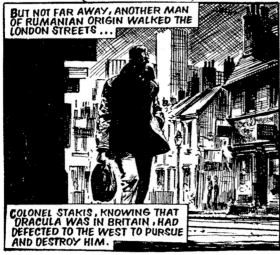

BUT NOT FAR AWAY, ANOTHER MAN OF RUMANIAN ORIGIN WALKED THE LONDON STREETS...

COLONEL STAKIS, KNOWING THAT DRACULA WAS IN BRITAIN, HAD DEFECTED TO THE WEST TO PURSUE AND DESTROY HIM.

STAKIS CARRIED THE WEAPONS OF THE VAMPIRE HUNTER WITH HIM...

A SIMPLE ARSENAL COMPARED WITH THAT FIEND'S POWERS...BUT THEY WILL DEFEAT HIM, IF I CAN JUST GET CLOSE ENOUGH TO USE THEM!

THE INJURED NIGHT-WORKER MANAGED TO ELUDE HIS PURSUERS...

I'VE LOST THOSE MANIACS... JUST GOT TO STOP AND CATCH ME BREATH!

HUH? WHAT'S THAT?

A PAIR OF EYES INSIDE THE PILLAR-BOX! IT AIN'T POSSIBLE!

COLLECTION TIMES

UURGH... SOME SORT OF MIST POURING OUT... CHOKING ME! NO! NOOOOO!

THE WORKER LAY DEAD... A VICTIM OF DRACULA'S UNNATURAL POWER. BUT...

IT— IT IS ALMOST DAWN. QUICKLY—MY POWER IS WANING— HELP ME TO MY REST-PLACE!

YES, MASTER...

IN A HOTEL, A LITTLE WAY AWAY...

IT TURNED OUT TO BE A WASTED NIGHT. YET I WAS SURE I CAME CLOSE TO FINDING THAT MONSTER. NOW I MUST SLEEP. I WILL NEED ALL MY STRENGTH FOR MY NEXT ENCOUNTER!

N- NOW STAY ON WATCH FOR THE VAMPIRE HUNTER! HE MAY YET FIND US!

YES, MASTER... NOW YOU MUST SLEEP.

HUNTERS! I HAVE KNOWN THEM FROM OLD, IN MY HOME-LAND. THEY HAVE PLAGUED ME EVER SINCE THE DRACULA NAME WAS FIRST HEARD! I REMEMBER ONE VAMPIRE HUNTER IN PARTICULAR...

Next Issue: Once upon a time in Transylvania!

AIEE! IT'S HIM! DRACULA!

STAY CALM — HE CANNOT ENTER A CHURCH...CAN YOU, DEMON?

INDEED NOT. BUT THEN, I DO NOT NEED TO!

MY VICTIMS WILL COME TO ME!

A FEW HOURS LATER...

DRIVER, HALT!

OH, NO! TH-THOSE TWO WOMEN ARE UNDER HIS SPELL!

STOP THEM! STOP THEM!

DEAD, WITH TWO FAMILIAR PUNCTURE MARKS ON THE NECK. IT SEEMS WE HAVE ARRIVED!

COME, CARL. WE'LL STAY THE REST OF THE NIGHT HERE . . !

...FOR TOMORROW WE TRAVEL TO CASTLE DRACULA! THERE WE WILL END FOREVER THIS REIGN OF EVIL!

 Next issue: Dracula's Dinner Guests!

ONDON, 1984. DRACULA, THE LEGENDARY VAMPIRE ROM EASTERN EUROPE, HAD LEARNED OF COLONEL AKIS, A WOULD-BE VAMPIRE HUNTER. NOW, HIS HOUGHTS TURNED TO TRANSYLVANIA IN 1892, AND O ANOTHER MAN WHO HAD HUNTED HIM...

"THE CREATURES OF THE NIGHT ALERTED ME THAT I HAD GUESTS BUT INSTEAD OF ORDERING THEM TO ATTACK, I TOLD THEM TO LET THE CARRIAGE PASS. IN SOME BIZARRE WAY I CRAVED 'COMPANY' THAT NIGHT ...

ALEXANDER QUINN! I CURSE MYSELF FOR NOT REALISING AT ONCE, THE VERY REAL THREAT HE POSED! HE WAS JUST A MORTAL, IT'S TRUE, YET HE WAS ABLE TO CHALLENGE ME, THE PRINCE OF DARKNESS!

SCREAM
SCRIPT: SIMON FURMAN
ART: ERIC BRADBURY
LETTERING: J. ALDRICH

AT LAST, CASTLE DRACULA NEARS... IT SEEMS WE MUST CONFRONT THE VAMPIRE WHEN HE IS AT HIS MOST DANGEROUS — AT NIGHT!

THE DRACULA FILE

WE MUST LULL THE CREATURE INTO A FALSE SENSE OF SECURITY. YOU MUST PLAY THE PART OF MY SERVANT, CARL.

MY VISITORS HAVE ARRIVED!

AH, REEVES. WE HAVE GUESTS ...

SHOULD I MAKE THEM, ER ... WELCOME?

Scream Holiday Specials:

Art:

Eric Bradbury   1986

Geoff Senior   1985 & 1987

Keith Page   1988

...AND MY MOST DEADLY WEAPON IS THE SILVER *STAKE* TO DRIVE INTO THAT DEVIL'S HEART.

FOR THE NEXT THREE WEEKS, STAKIS VISITED STATION AFTER STATION ON THE LONDON UNDERGROUND...

NO SIGN OF THE VAMPIRE...

MAYBE HE HAS MOVED TO NEW HUNTING GROUNDS...

TONIGHT IS A FULL MOON, HIS TRADITIONAL HUNTING-TIME. MAYBE *THAT* WILL TEMPT HIM OUT...

THEN, JUST AS THE RUMANIAN WAS CROSSING A SUBWAY...

A *CLOAKED* FIGURE COMING ALONG THE PASSAGEWAY! IT MUST BE HIM!

SECONDS LATER –

NOW, UNDEAD ONE –

WHAT THE ?

STAKIS REALISED HE HAD MADE A MISTAKE...

IT WAS A HARMLESS MUSICIAN RETURNING FROM A NIGHT-CONCERT AND I ALMOST KILLED HIM! I MUST FLEE...

BUT AS STAKIS CROSSED THE BRIDGE...

A TRAIN PULLING IN AND SOMETHING PERCHED ON ITS ROOF... *A BAT!*

IT IS *HE*... DRACULA IS HERE AFTER ALL! AND HIS PREY IS THAT POOR TRAMP IN THE TRAIN CARRIAGE...

I'LL NEVER GET THERE IN TIME...

THE DRACULA FILE

ALL THE FUN OF THE FAIR...

THE THRILLS OF THE GHOST TRAIN...

GHOST TRAIN

HEY... LOOK AT THAT. LET'S GIVE IT A TRY!

COULD BE FUN, MAYBE WE CAN DUFF THE PLACE UP A BIT...

OKAY, POP, IF THIS THING FAILS TO SCARE US... WE'LL WANT OUR MONEY BACK!

YEAH... WITH INTEREST!

HAW, HAW! LOOK AT THAT!

POOR THING LOOKS FRIGHTENED... GOT NO GUTS!

IT'S GOT NOTHIN' NOW!

THIS PLACE IS PATHETIC!

LET'S SMASH IT *ALL* UP!

HEY...THAT ONE'S NOT SO BAD.

IT'S SUPPOSED TO BE THAT DRACULA BLOKE!

FOOLS...I *AM* THE VAMPIRE!

WH-WHY ARE WE STOPPING?

YOU GREAT COWARDS... IT'S ONLY SOME GEEZER DRESSED-UP!

WATCH ME GIVE HIM A FEW THUMPS. HE JUST WANTS TO SCARE US...

I JUST WANT YOUR...*BLOOD!*

SCREAMS FROM INSIDE THE GHOST TRAIN WERE NOT UNUSUAL. BUT THIS ONE WAS *FOR REAL!*

ARRRRRGH!

GHOST TRAIN

ALL THE *FEAR* OF THE FAIR!

THE HUNTER...

THE VAMPIRE IS CLOSE...I AM SURE OF IT!

TH-THANK GOODNESS YOU'RE HERE. IN...INSIDE THERE! FOUR KIDS... ALL MURDERED! HORRIBLE, IT IS...

MAYBE *THIS* IS DRACULA'S WORK...

A BAT LEAVES THE BUILDING! THAT DEVIL HAS CHANGED FROM ITS HUMAN FORM...

IT GOES INTO THE TOP OF THE HELTER-SKELTER...IF ONLY I COULD BE SURE IT WASN'T JUST AN ORDINARY BAT...

A FEW MINUTES LATER, THE HUNTER KNEW THE TRUTH...

A DEAD MAN!

EAAAARGH!

HE MUST HAVE COLLAPSED ON THE WAY DOWN!

THIS IS NO NATURAL DEATH! THE BITE MARKS... THE MARK OF THE FANGS! DRACULA *IS* UP THERE!

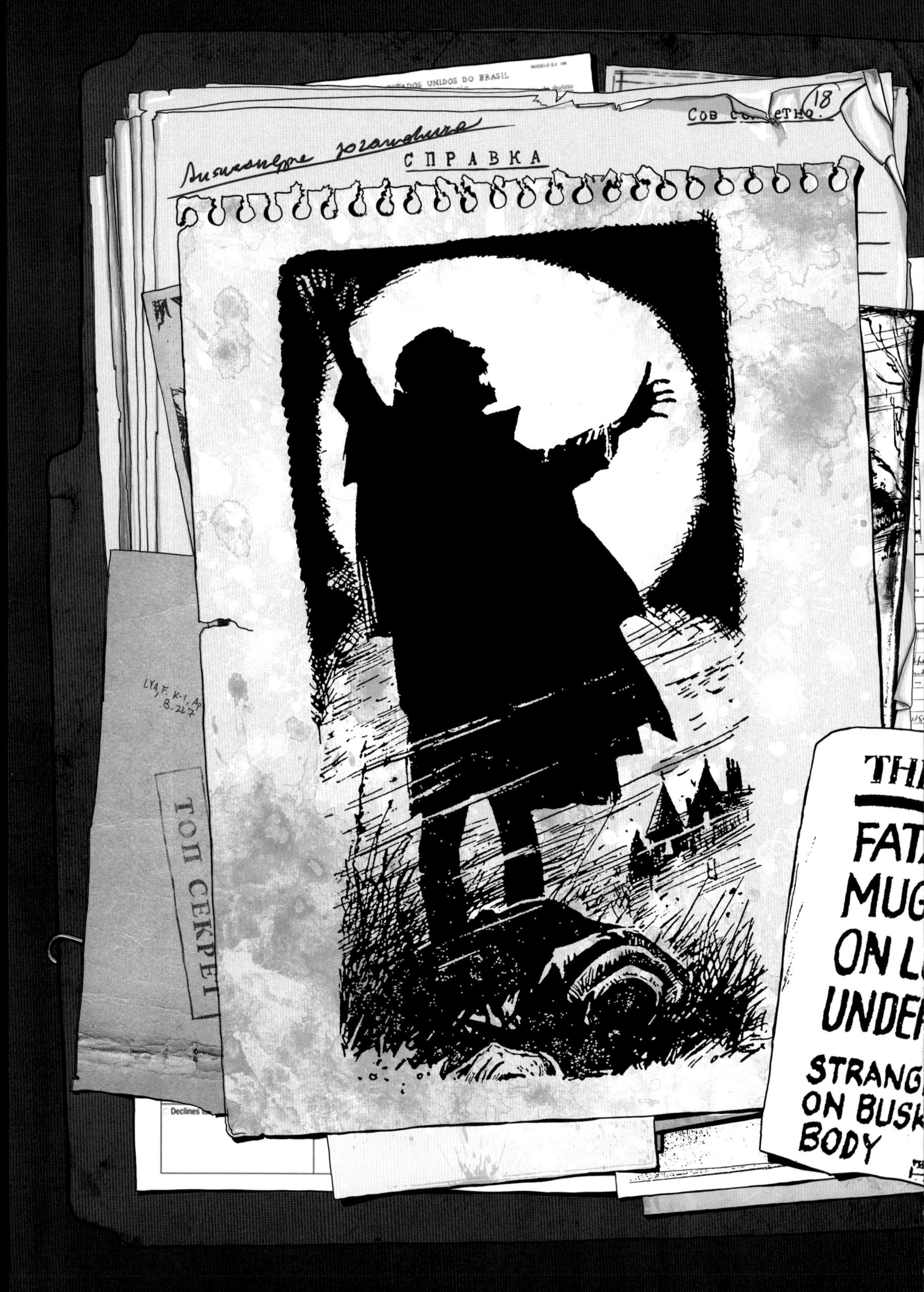

СПРАВКА
СОВ СЕКРЕТНО
18
ESTADOS UNIDOS DO BRASIL
LYA, F. K-1, AP. B-227
ТОП СЕКРЕТ
Declines
FATA
MUG
ON L
UNDER
STRANG
ON BUSK
BODY

The following two pages feature **Eric Bradbury** artwork that was never originally published in the weekly issues of **Scream!** or any of the holiday specials.

The story featured in the 1986 holiday special shares a continuity with the two pages presented here (same setting, same characters), so it would be safe to assume that they were originally part of the same **Dracula File** story arc and had been planned to run in the comic before it was cancelled.

We would like to thank David McDonald for making us aware that these pages existed and to Barrie Tomlinson for agreeing that they could be supplied to us for this collection.

GHASTLY'S DRACULA QUIZ

Right, my fiendish friends! If you're fans of our Dracula File story, then you should enjoy having a bite at this little Count Dracula Quiz I've devised for you. Just answer A, B or C (no, they're not blood groups, you dummies) to the 10 questions. The answers are at the foot of the page.

1 Dracula was based on a real man who earned himself the nickname 'The Impaler', (sounds like a nice character, eh?). Can you tell us what his first name was?
(a) COUNT; (b) VLAD; (c) BORIS.

2 The first screen Dracula was played by which of the following actors?
(a) MAX SCHRECK; (b) CHRISTOPHER LEE; (c) BELA LUGOSI.

3 Who wrote the book 'Dracula'? Was it . . .
(a) MARY SHELLEY; (b) BRAM STOKER; (c) THE BROTHERS GRIMM.

4 Which of the following creatures can't Dracula turn into?
(a) A WOLF; (b) A BAT; (c) A HAWK.

5 Which plant is said to help ward off the Count?
(a) CACTUS; (b) GARLIC; (c) RUBBER.

6 When Peter Cushing appears in a Dracula film, he usually plays the Count's sworn enemy. The name of this character is. . .
(a) VAN HELSING; (b) VAN HIRE; (c) VAN DER GRAFF.

7 Which of the following cannot kill Dracula?
(a) A SILVER BULLET; (b) FIRE; (c) A STAKE THROUGH THE HEART.

8 Where is Dracula's castle?
(a) HOLLYWOOD; (b) ENGLAND; (c) TRANSYLVANIA.

9 What is Dracula's staple diet?
(a) STEAK; (b) BLOOD; (c) STAPLES.

10 What do you consider is the best way to greet Dracula?

A WOTCHER, MATE! B HELLO, SIR! C GOODBYE!

NOW CHECK YOUR ANSWERS . . . IF YOU DARE! (Each correct answer earns you two marks— on the neck!)

(1) b: Vlad the Impaler was Prince of the state of Wallachia around the end of 15th century. He is said to have had 10,000 Turkish prisoners impaled on wooden stakes. He belonged to the 'Order of the Dragon', (Drakul meant Dragon) so he adopted the name 'Dracula'; (2) a: Max Schreck in the 1922 silent film 'Nosferatu'. Bela Lugosi took the role in 1931, and Christopher Lee in 1958. (3) b: Bram Stoker published in 1897. (4) c: A hawk. (5) b: Garlic. (6) a: Van Helsing. (7) a: (In legend a Silver Bullet is meant to kill a werewolf.) (8) c: Transylvania. (9) b: Blood – steak tends not to agree with him. (10) Take your pick – a: I don't fancy your chances, b: very polite – I'm sure he'd say thank you after drinking your blood, c: very sensible!

Scream! #10 - 26.05.84
Eric Bradbury

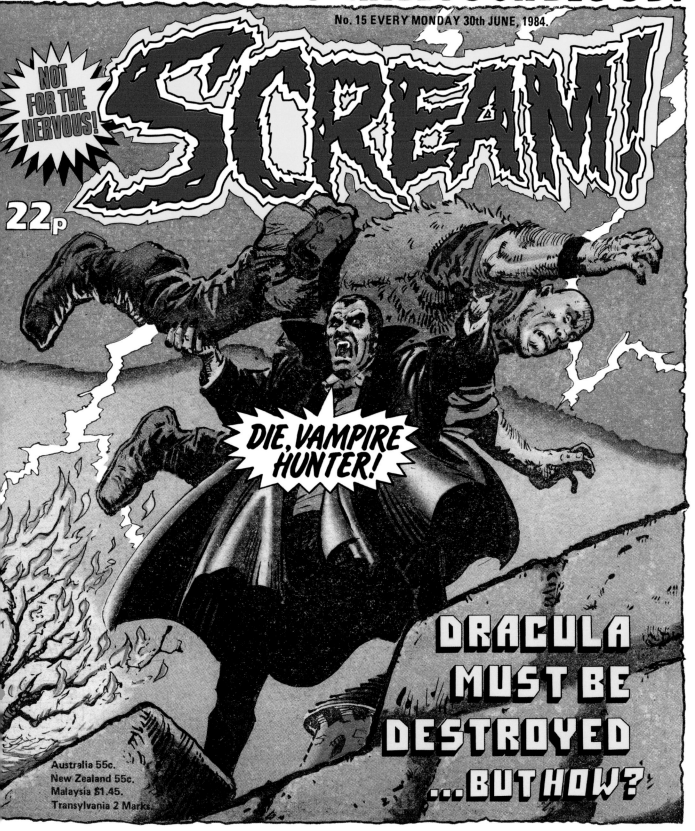

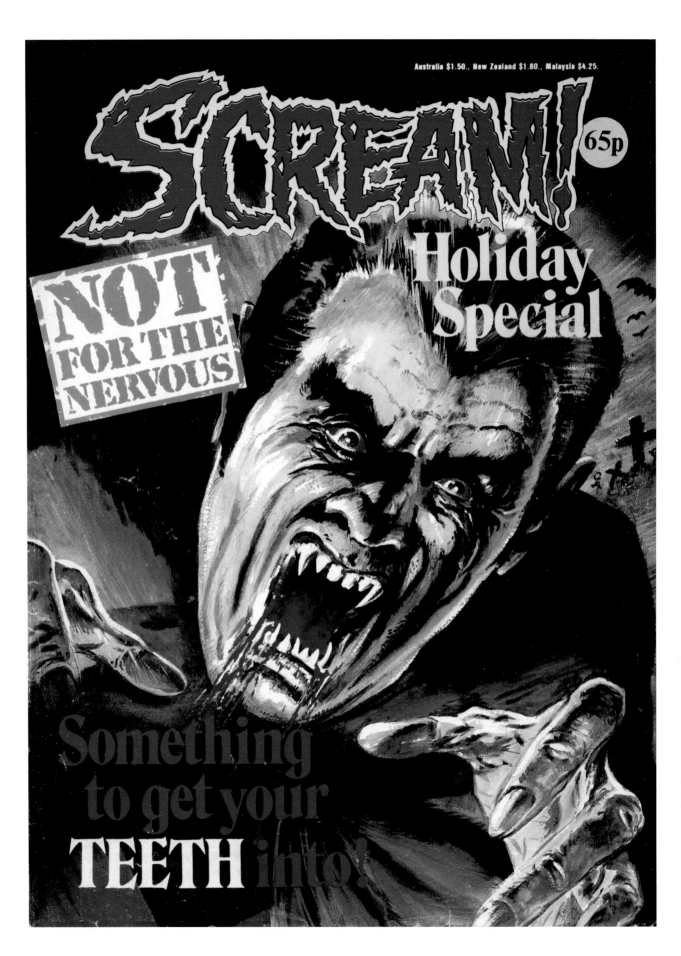

Scream! Holiday Special - 1986
Eric Bradbury

FEATURE
by: David McDonald

SILENT SCREAMS!

SCREAM! FIRST APPEARED ON THE NEWSAGENTS SHELVES IN 1984 AND CONSIDERING IT ONLY LASTED 15 ISSUES, IT HAS GARNERED A SUBSTANTIAL CULT FOLLOWING OVER THE YEARS.

PART OF THIS cult is due to its sudden disappearance from the newsagents, leading to rumours that parent's complaints had led to its hasty demise. In reality it was senior managements' unease with publishing a horror comic and also an industrial dispute which removed it from sale.

The majority of its cult following however came from the fact that it was simply a great comic! It had a mix of *Eagle* and *2000 AD* creators, a young and vibrant editorial team in Ian Rimmer and Simon Furman and the steady hand of Barrie Tomlinson overseeing the title.

Dracula was the face of *Scream!*, appearing on the cover of the first issue along with three other characters, the newsagent's flyer and even on the TV ad. Dracula's high profile in the UK in the eighties could be traced to Christopher Lee's hugely popular portrayal of the character in numerous Hammer films.

Barrie Tomlinson (*Scream!* creator) was tasked with producing the starting line up. I asked him what he recalled about the inclusion of a Dracula strip.

'I wanted to include Dracula because it is such a classic story, and I knew we had just the artist to draw it. Eric Bradbury's work was absolutely brilliant!'

Bradbury's art certainly fits with the tone of the Hammer Films with his fancy dress costumed Dracula. A British comic stalwart, Bradbury was no stranger to IPC comics' darker side. He was one of the artists on IPC's first proposed horror comics.

'Horror' was a dirty word in comics since the infamous EC comics line in the US. The furore over the book *Seduction of the Innocent*, by Fredric Wertham had led to the withdrawal of most American horror comics and the setting up of the Comics Code Authority of America.

These often lurid comics had a direct effect on UK comics, most importantly the setting up of *Eagle* in 1950. Rev. Marcus Morris, *Eagle's* editor, wanted a counterbalance to the four colour American comics that were increasingly available on British newsagent's shelves. Eagle was a roaring success, lasting 19 years and creating the icon that is *Dan Dare*. The events in the US made British publishers put horror out of sight, until in 1968, a young editor called Gil Page proposed a comic called *Blackjack*.

At that time something was always being worked on at Fleetway (IPC) - just in case the powers that he had to combat a title launched by their rivals in Dundee, D.C. Thomson. Most never saw the light of day, for a variety of reasons and were eventually broken up and their contents dispersed among existing titles.

Smash!, which had been published by Odhams, was a mix of American Marvel and DC reprint with some original humour and adventure content. Odhams, while owned by IPC for a while, took until 1969 before it became fully 'absorbed' into IPC. *Smash*! was relaunched as a traditional IPC comic like *Valiant* or *Lion*, but with a twist.

Above: *Scream!* Promo art.
Below: *Misty* cover
by Shirley Bellwood.

Gil Page explained in an interview in Hibernia's *The Fleetway Files*: *'It (Smash!) was the fortunate recipient of some classic strips from a then controversial horror title named Blackjack, which was never launched. To this day I can remember that every story from that dummy that went into another title shot straight to the top of the readers' popularity polls that we used to run.'* *Blackjack* was proposed to have the following characters included in its launch issue; *Janus Stark*, *Master of the Marsh*, the Bradbury drawn *Cursitor Doom*, *The Pillater Peril* and *Simon Test*. Hardly the scariest line up, but all great tales in their own right with *Cursitor Doom* being the closest to proper horror.

Gil Page was Managing Editor by the time *Scream!* was launched in 1984 and was very supportive of it, he recalled, also in *The Fleetway Files*, *'Scream! was good and I was certainly responsible for pushing for a horror title to be launched. I'd never forgotten Blackjack! But the whole thing was a real can of worms. Big IPC was so frightened of it, we used to have a censorship meeting to examine each page before it was sent to press!'*

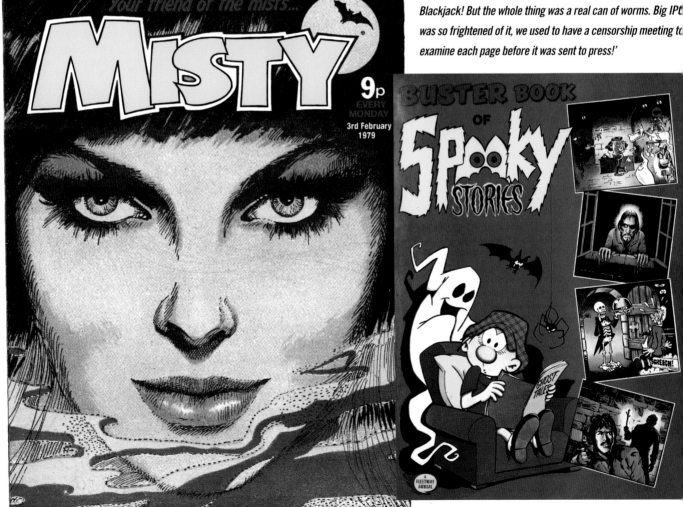

Dez Skinn, renowned editor of *Warrior* and creator of the *Doctor Who* comic and *Starburst* magazine, learned some of his trade while working as a sub-editor on IPC humour titles in the early seventies. On his website DezSkinn.com he recalls his suggestion for a weekly horror comic he called *Chiller*. Producing a dummy issue, Skinn passed it onto management. To his disappointment, it became the *Buster Book of Spooky Stories* instead. Although this wasn't exactly what he had in mind, Skinn was able to commission some impressive artists for the two annuals, including Eric Bradbury, Ian Kennedy and a young Dave Gibbons.

The humour department under Bob Paynter twice produced 'scary' comics in the form of *Shiver and Shake* and *Monster Fun*, and while these were well produced and fondly remembered, they were light on scares and heavy on laughs. *Monster Fun* is worth mentioning for Leo Baxendale's brilliant *BadTime BedTime* pullout section that came with the comic, featuring his unique and witty take on bedtime stories.

One can hardly mention the humour comic section and horror without mentioning the great Ken Reid. Having created *Roger the Dodger* and *Jonah* among others for DC Thomson, he moved to Odhams in the sixties and created many characters including the popular *Frankie Stein*.

Frankie Stein could be seen as the start of Reid's move toward "body horror" culminating in 'Ricky Rubberneck' AKA *Faceache* in *Jet* for IPC in 1971. *Faceache* was Reid's longest running strip which transferred to *Buster* in 1972. He continued to draw it until his death in 1987.

While *Faceache* is probably his best known work, he also produced *Martha's Monster Make Up*, a female *Faceache* for *Monster Fun* and the puntastic *Tom Horrors World* for *Wow!*

None of this however tops his work on the single page illustrations - *Creepy Creations*, *Most Wanted* and *World Wide Weirdies* he did for Bob Paynter's titles *Shiver and Shake* and *Whoopee*. These were reader's suggestions of inanimate objects brought to life in the most disturbing Reid fashion!

Above: *Faceache* by Ken Reid & Dave Gibbons *Ghost Pilot* from the *Buster Book of Spooky Stories*

One of Reid's creations that had the potential to be his most disturbing never saw the light of day. Pat Mills has the details in his book *Be Pure! Be Vigilant! Behave! 2000 AD and Judge Dredd: The Secret History*; *'A few weeks before 2000 AD was due to go to press, I learnt that there was a brilliant Ken Reid cartoon strip he had produced for a dummy that had never been published!!! Jack Le Grand thought it was disgusting and condemned it to the vaults. It concerned the hideous mutant survivor of a nuclear war who had a horrible "thing" on his back and every week he would try and kill himself. But each week the thing on his back would prevent him. So if he jumped off a cliff, the thing would turn into a propeller and fly him to safety etc. You can just imagine how Ken would have drawn it! How deliciously foul and what a wonderful contrast to all those saccharine, formula strips in Whoopee! et al. Just what I needed for the back cover of 2000 AD. I had 100 per cent power to do what I wanted with 2000 AD, so I requisitioned the strip from the vaults. But the old regime told me that it had mysteriously "disappeared" and could not be found. Yeah, right.'*

Mills was heavily involved in the creation of the most successful of IPC's attempts at a horror comic, *Misty*. IPC's rival DC Thomson had taken the lead in 1976 and produced *'An All Mystery Comic for Girls'* called *Spellbound*. Whether or not IPC were heartened by the lack of outcry over this new title or its relative success, *Misty* was in the planning stage by the end of 1977. IPC wanted Mills to create the comic, in the same fashion as he did with *Action* and *2000 AD*, but he felt with the success he enjoyed with these titles he should be given a share of whatever profits the new comic would garner. This was not forthcoming from IPC so instead he took an advisory role with the creation of the comic.

Girl's comics had a different style of storytelling than boys. Boy's comics in general relied on action (read violence in a lot of cases), to propel the story. Action was less apparent in girl's comics, so better characterisation and more sophisticated storytelling were used to tell the story.

Misty used this to its advantage. Girl's comics often used a cruel parent or teacher as a foil to the heroine. So to add a little magic and supernatural to the mix along with top quality creators, rather than all out scares you get an eeriness and impending sense of dread from the comic. Lasting two years, it avoided the adverse attention of IPC management. I asked Pat how the title managed this; *'IPC management backed me. I could do what I wanted, because I could deliver the goods. So they backed my original vision on Misty. They knew it would sell, because I was using a succesful formula'*

Cut-out and collect this side-splitting series of wonderful weirdies!

WORLD-WIDE WEIRDIES

NO. 1 THE PETRIFYING PYRAMID

£2 TO BE WON EVERY WEEK!

We want to take a weird and whacky look at anything or any place in the World . . . got any ideas? Send your sketch to "WORLD-WIDE WEIRDIES" at the WHOOPEE! AND SHIVER & SHAKE address — and make sure the title and your name and address is shown clearly. Each week we will select one of the ideas and make a finished drawing from it! £2 will be awarded to the sender of each chosen picture.

Misty merged with *Tammy* in 1980 and the title remained titled *Tammy and Misty* until 1984. *Misty* annuals were produced until 1986 and it had the distinction of being the only Girls' comic to have a 'Best of' monthly which lasted 8 issues.

The early eighties saw a rapid decline in comic sales with titles cancelled and new launches failing. Management knew there was a possible market for horror orientated comics, but while the Humour and Girls department had attempted and had some success with the genre, the Boys department never did.

In 1983 that changed. *Fantasy Advertiser*, the British comic newszine, in its eighty first issue from October 1983, report news of a possible new comic from IPC, as follows; *'A Mystery Horror had been developed, but may or may not be ever give the go-ahead to be printed. At one time called Phantom, it's now called Shriek… or Scream!'*

And the rest is history!

GERRY FINLEY-DAY

One of the most prolific writers in the comic's history, **Gerry Finley-Day** holds a special place in many *2000 AD* fans' hearts as the creator of classics like *Rogue Trooper*, *Fiends of the Eastern Front* and *The V.C.s*, as well as *Harry 20 on the High Rock* and *Ant Wars*.

A keen "ideas man", Finley-Day's concepts of the horrors future warfare had in store were key to both *Rogue* and *The V.C.s'* continuing popularity, ensuring that their recent return to the Galaxy's Greatest Comic was well-received.

Finley-Day also scripted episodes of *Judge Dredd* and *Dan Dare*, and co-scripted much of *Invasion!* (and entirely scripted the prequel story, '*Disaster 1990!*').

SIMON FURMAN

Best known for writing *Transformers* comics, **Simon Furman** was instrumental in making Marvel UK a success. During the eighties and nineties he worked on many titles for them, including the aforementioned *Transformers* and also *Action Force*, *Thundercats*, *Doctor Who* Magazine as well as two series he helped create – *Dragon's Claws* and *Death's Head*.

Simon has written several issues of *Judge Dredd: Lawman of the Future* and shared scripting chores with Dan Abnett on Marvel's *Guardians of the Galaxy*.

ERIC BRADBURY

The great **Eric Bradbury** began his comic career at *Knockout*, working on such humour strips as *Blossom* and *Our Ernie*. He moved onto the adventure western *Lucky Logan*, sharing art chores with Mike Western (Bradbury would go on to ink Western's pencils on *The Leopard from Lime Street*). High profile work on *Mytek the Mighty* (Valiant & Vulcan), the *House of Dolmann* (Valiant), *Von Hoffman's Invasion* (Jet!), *Death Squad* (Battle), *Hook Jaw* (Action) and *Doomlord* (The Eagle) followed.

Bradbury has been described as an 'unsung hero' of *2000 AD*, having contributed to many popular strips in the long-running sci-fi comic. His credits in the 'Galaxy's Greatest comic' include *Rogue Trooper*, *Tharg the Mighty*, *Invasion* and *The Mean Arena*.